Stars

~

the real pictures

by Nick Addey

 Little Pig Publications

Published by

Little Pig Publications, Rossbrin, Schull, Co. Cork, Ireland

www.littlepigpublications.com

Thanks to all those who have added bits and pieces to this project. A special 'thank you' to Carola for her input and patience.

ISBN   978-0-9560460-0-0

Cover background from a Rob Keywood photograph
H.C.Berann's Jungfrau summer map courtesy Jungfraubahn, Interlaken, Switzerland

Printed in Ireland by Colour Books Ltd, Dublin.

Introduction

How many times has the question been asked 'Where are the real pictures in the stars?' Answer comes there none, or if it does it runs something like: To the people who named the stars 'the precise resemblance of a group of a dozen stars to a Bear, a Lion or a Hunter was unimportant.'*

Can this really be true? I find it hard to believe that our ancestors, far more in tune with nature than we can ever be, would name the stars without good reason. Why call a star the Bear if no bear is to be seen? More likely it is us, moving further and further from the natural world, who have forgotten how to look.

The night sky is full of shapes: curves, lines, squares and complex patterns, all of which, with a little practice, can be readily identified and returned to time and again. Our ancestors would surely have used such recognisable shapes for learning and naming the stars. If this is so then the creatures and characters they came to know, name and love, thousands of years ago, are still up there, poised, and ready for a grand cosmic comeback.

In the beauty of a starry night I find that the straight lines of modern constellations have no relevance; interest wanes. Yet the myth, embedded in ancient lore, is compelling; Adhara, Aldebaran, Mirzam - mystic words from a mystery world. Delve deeper and you find that these old Arabic, pre-Roman star names translate as: the Virgins, the Follower and the Announcer. Intriguing titles whose origins - the real pictures - are said not to exist.

Poppycock! Guided by star names I have pieced together many gratifyingly realistic images. Perhaps not surprisingly these echo well-known mythological stories. Within Auriga: the Charioteer, for example, we find the stars Menkalinan: Shoulder of the Rein-holder, Capella: She-goat, and Maaz: He-goat. Not far away, in Ursa Major (aka Arthur's Chariot), there is a fine image of a chariot; all these are essential elements of Norse mythology where Thor, the great god, has goats to pull his chariot.

From 'The Mapping of the Heavens' by P. Whitfield.

Once I'd spotted the star/story connection it became possible to work from the stories to find other pictures, ones not suggested by star names. This huge, exciting field (beyond the scope of this book, but the essence of the Little Pig Star Book series (see p.48)) reveals the way storytellers used star pictures to construct their stories. The example below gives a very basic insight as to how our ancestors put night sky pictures into words:

Finnian loomed on him as a portent and a terror; but he had no fear of Time. Indeed he was the foster-brother of Time, and so disdainful of the bitter god that he did not even disdain him; he leaped over the scythe, he dodged under it, and the sole occasions on which Time laughs is when he chances on Tuan, the son of Cairill, the son of Muredac Red-neck.*

Delphinus

Lyra

Aquila

* 'The story of Tuan Mac Cairill' Irish Mythology

The contents of this book hint at revelations to come, for once we have the real pictures a forgotten world appears. A world of myth and legend, yes, but also a world so deeply woven into the fabric of our lives that we have lost sight of it completely.

For now though, let's focus on images - human, animal and artefact - found through star or constellation names.

There is nothing complicated about the images and they need minimum imagination to see. As it was with those join-the-dots drawings we did as children, so it is with the stars – join them correctly and the images leap out at you. Curiously it is blackness that makes them bold, not the stars. A good image will be surrounded by free space, an absence of stars, blackness. Inside, also, there will be no distracting stars; again, blackness.

You do need to be observant and realistic, able to pick out the defining features of an earthly item before you can see its image in the night sky. If, for instance, you're happy with the notion of prancing bears with long, bright tails, then you will never see the greatest bear that ever there was (see p.18), and that would be a shame.

Traditional Great Bear image

Ursa Major

This image comes from the Vienna Manuscript c.1440

What do you see when you look up at the stars? Perhaps you can recognise the Big Dipper (aka the Plough) and Orion's Belt but, if you are like I was a few years ago, that might be about it.

One night, however, I saw the Fish and my life changed dramatically. The Fish was such a perfect picture, a salmon leaping up a waterfall, that I was hooked. Back indoors I hunted high and low for a long neglected rotating star chart. Once found I saw that the Fish was in Perseus, a constellation I'd never heard of.

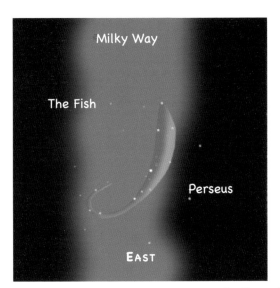

Disregarding my stellar inexperience the quest for real pictures began. It is amazing what your mind can do with a few pinpricks of light, especially with a little practice. However, it does help to be prompted, for the night sky is an awesome place. So, for my first target I chose the Great Bear. Mistake number one. Frustration, disappointment, chill set in. Basically I hadn't a clue at that stage, the Fish was a fluke and I was floundering.

Gradually though, over the months, ideas and stars came together and pictures started to form. Years were to pass, however, before the Great Bear finally revealed itself.

Although many pictures have taken me years to find, it will take you only moments to see the simple ones. Intricate shapes like the Great Bear may take a little longer, but don't worry if you can't see a picture straight away. Many times I've had an inkling of an image one night; on the second night it starts to solidify; by the third or fourth night all the stars are in their place and the picture works. Patience, like a clear sky, is essential. So is timing. Each picture has an optimum moment; be it the location e.g. near the horizon, or be it the light/darkness of the sky. Usually it's both. Pictures, it seems, present themselves only when they are ready.

How on earth does one start? The stars look chaotic to a casual observer. On any one night you might see two thousand or so, scattered everywhere. What's more, they are not in the same positions that they were six months ago when you last took a peek. Tricky stuff for a beginner, but fear not, after a few nights star-watching patterns will emerge.

Here is the most useful piece of advice a novice star-watcher will ever hear: 'Start before it gets dark.' Seriously, the best time to get outside is at dusk, just before star-break (when the stars first appear). The second most useful tip involves hot-water bottles, gloves, scarves and a comfy (swivel) chair.

So, you are sitting comfortably, you are warm, you have clear skies and clear horizons. You are lucky! I suspect most of us suffer, to some degree, from light and atmospheric pollution, blocked horizons, chilly breezes and frozen feet. That's normal. It's why I ask you not to take this book lightly, for the project has been a test of endurance. Although blessed with unpolluted skies and low horizons, the raw chill of a winter's night is not always easy to face. Nonetheless, on looking up...

...you see a star; the first to appear. You rotate your star-chart and decide the star is Capella. So far so good.

Then another star appears, much too close. Humph. Is one of them a planet, or are you really looking at Castor and Pollux?

More stars appear and you recognise the pattern. Now it's clear; the first 'star' is a planet.*

Patterns make for good reference, they create order and establish identity. In this case you need the She-goat pattern, for Capella means She-goat, and Capella is her eye.

This system of identification only works if the pictures are real. Abstract pictures are, by their lack of definition, hard to define; which is why, to the people who named the stars, the precise resemblance of a group of stars to a Bear, a Lion or a Hunter was, in fact, vitally important.

Finally, before the show begins, should anyone deride your search for real pictures with the flippant remark: 'You can make anything you like in the stars' well, I've been trying for years, and you can't. You can only make what is there, and what is there has been seen and used by our ancestors to create a visual feast that is truly out of this world!

*Planets move around, so do not feature in any of the real pictures.

Let's start with something nice and easy
The Flying Swan

(constellations Lyra & Cygnus: the Swan)

The Flying Swan is a good image to begin with. It is easy to locate, nestling between Deneb and Vega (two bright stars that grace our summer nights) and it is a comfortable size to see.

Some pictures are really huge, and our eyes have to move around the whole shape in order to work them out. Other pictures can be so small you have to focus intently upon those stars; the swan though is just right.

In the best pictures the brightest stars will be at defining points, i.e. eyes, head, joints, feet etc. In the case of the Flying Swan they are at the head (brightest), tail and leading edge of the wing. Fainter stars fill in the detail; look carefully in the night sky for the tail shape and beak.

The Flying Swan, like many star pictures, does not confine itself to its constellation* boundary. Why should it? The lines that bind stars together are merely for human convenience.

*For standard constellation boundaries please refer to regular guide books.

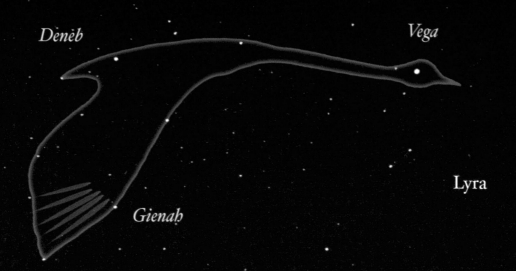

Cygnus

Deneb

Vega

Gienah

Lyra

Deneb means Tail.
Gienah means Wing.
Vega has something to
do with an eagle.

Best viewing: summer, when Cygnus flies high in the south. When in the east the Swan appears more like a hand pointing up, in the west it becomes a cow!

(Times and locations are approximate. Rotating star-charts are ideal for working out exactly what stars

And now for something even easier!
The Tent
(constellation Corvus)

Al Chiba means the Tent and with so few stars to work with it's easy to see a tent in Corvus: the Crow. Nothing tricky at all. A real joy, on my discovering this tent, was to find (on a clear night) that it is fitted with guy ropes. I guess it gets windy up there. You could use the two faint internal stars to put a billow in either side of the tent.

There are plenty of other tents in the sky, all with varying perspective. This one appears to be below the viewer, as if pitched in a valley, as does a very similar tent-shape in Cetus. Other tents can be seen on a plain (try in Aquarius) or up the top of a hill (try in Cassiopeia when high in the sky).

The Crow itself isn't so easy to see, but I suspect Corvus is just the beak. Any suggestions welcome.

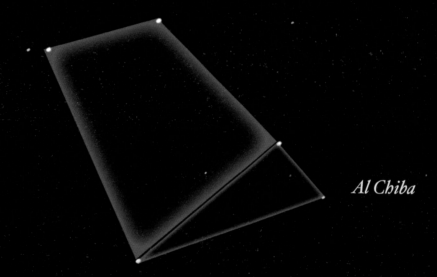

Corvus

Al Chiba

Best viewing: spring and early summer, when Corvus is in the south.

Double trouble with
The Twins
(constellation Gemini: the Twins)

Humans come in all shapes and sizes, they also come in all sorts of poses. These are reflected in the stars, or rather, our minds recognise these earthly shapes and project them onto star patterns. Which, presumably, is how the Twins came by their reputation as gourmands.

As eating and drinking have changed little over the years we should have no problem spotting which of the Twins is drinking and which is eating. The position of hand (star) relative to head determines whether a character is eating or drinking. Should there be any confusion Pollux translates as Much Wine.

Twins, to be unambiguously portrayed, have to be joined. It's no good showing two people holding hands or two children hugging each other.

Gemini

Castor

Pollux

Pollux is the drinker. Curiously it is a slightly red star, just like an alcoholic's face.

The body is made from stars of equal strength.

Note the twin stars at each foot.

The star, Wasat, the Twin's midriff, means Middle.

Procyon

Best viewing: November to May - quite an obliging pair. In May they seem to walk on the northwestern horizon. Worth checking out.

Supplanter and Deceiver
The Follower
(constellation Taurus)

All sorts of poses... some of which may not be fit for family viewing! It's fun, though, and the stars will test your mental agility. For this narrow-focus picture you'll need the specs if you are short-sighted; the stars will test your eyesight, too.

Aldebaran (like James and Jacob) means the Follower. The given explanation for the name (i.e. Aldebaran follows the Pleiades star cluster through the sky) is, in my opinion, of dubious worth. This crouching, furtive figure surely would have been of more interest to our storytelling forebears.

Should you be able to work out who or what the Follower is following, then you're in for an awesome treat. If not you'll have to wait for the revelations of Book X (see p.48).

Of course, the Follower might not make it. I'd say there is a good chance he'll get eaten. By who or what? Answers to the www.realstarpictures.com website. The first ten that match my scenario will receive a Little Pig book.

Taurus

Aldebaran

The trick is to see Aldebaran
as a lamp, held close to the
ground, as if the figure is
following a trail at night.

Best viewing: autumn in the east, but visible until spring. The correct name
for this particular group of stars is the Hyades – rather similar to Hades,
wherein lives Lucifer, the Bringer of Light. Curious?

A load of
Bull

(constellations Auriga, Orion & Taurus: the Bull)

We are starting to get bigger and bolder now, rightfully so as this huge bull's head is a work of art.

Aldebaran is the bright eye, the clue to this coming from a close neighbour star, Ain, meaning the Eye. Perhaps, as there are so many overlapping pictures, some fainter stars adopted the main stars' secondary names.

That the Bull is working can be seen from the yoke around its neck. You can see the yoke by itself, ending in a point near Aldebaran. Without the yoke and with its head down, the Bull could be charging. If you look forward of the Bull, into Perseus, you might get the impression of a shaft or an elongated, twisted horn.

As with all bright star pictures the best way to find the Bull is to start at star-break, or when the moon is bright. Once you have the main feature stars it is easier to fill in with the fainter ones.

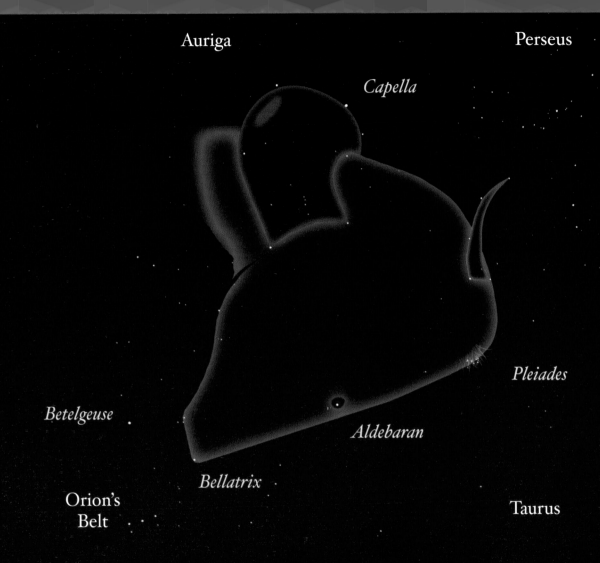

Auriga

Perseus

Capella

Pleiades

Betelgeuse

Aldebaran

Bellatrix

Orion's
Belt

Taurus

Best viewing: springtime, with Orion out west. Although visible all winter
the bull starts working only when it gets its head down.
The Pleiades provides the peculiar tuft of hair that bulls have on

Opposite the Bull we have
The Bear

(constellation Ursa Major: the Great Bear)

Anyone who has seen the traditional image of the Ursa Major bear might well lament 'But where are the real pictures?' for those who have even the slimmest grasp of animal anatomy will know - bears do not have tails.

On top of this tailed abomination (see p.5) lies the claim that it is a great bear - it certainly doesn't look it. No wonder some folk shake their heads and give up.

Bears are wonderful beasts and unless starving or provoked will steer well clear of us. However, should you corner one, or threaten a mother's cub, then the last thing you might see, before being slashed to oblivion, is an image like this.

Ursa Minor means Little Bear; look carefully for that tearful beast. That's two of the Three Bears. Where's Mummy Bear? She's in Pegasus, drinking from, say, a pool, or even nibbling the back end of a Dolphin.

Ursa Major

Dubhe

Dubhe means Bear

The secret to star bears is the pair of stars at the mouth; one indicating the nose, the other the distinctive drooping lower lip.

Best viewing: summer, when Ursa Major is in the northwest. Look carefully for the two faint stars that complete the triangular head.

Almost every star of Ursa Major is used to create the image, so be careful and patient when tracking this bear.

Along with the Bear we find
Arthur

(a great warrior, whose name means Bear)

This magnificent image is a must-see. The bright feet, planted firmly on the northern horizon, are the best starting point. The arm, up-thrust in salute or command, can be seen in conjunction with the faint but distinctive V-shaped Coma Berenices, which becomes a flail whirled around the great warrior's head.

The warrior is wearing a dark helmet, or has a lot of facial hair, as there are no features to his head save his eyes. These are faint and you will need a clear night to make them out, but they are there, staring down at you.

As Ursa Major sinks towards the horizon you should, with a slight adjustment, be able to turn him into a cavalryman. As such could he be one of the Four Riders of the Apocalypse?

Coma Berenices means the Hair of Berenices. Berenices was an Egyptian queen who, the stories say, offered her hair to the gods in exchange for the safe return from battle of her warrior husband. The normal interpretation is that the offering was hair from her head... my eyes beg to differ.

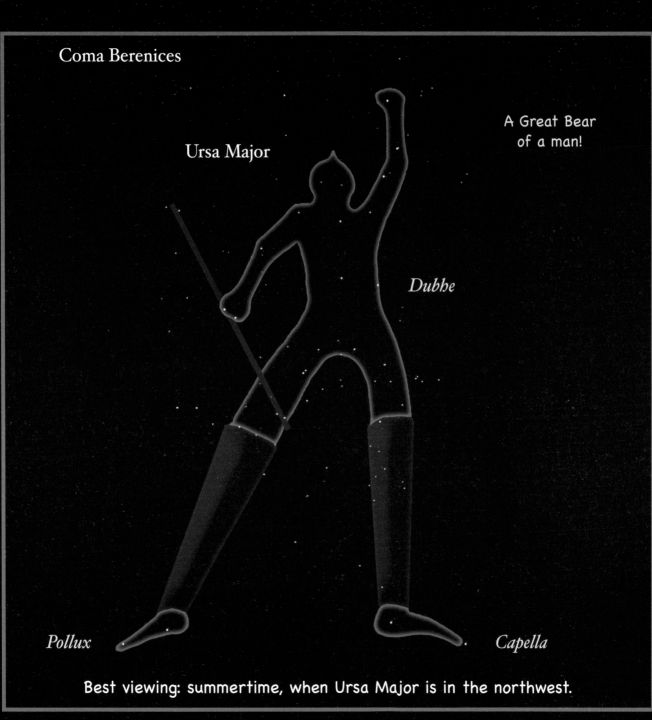

Coma Berenices

Ursa Major

A Great Bear
of a man!

Dubhe

Pollux

Capella

Best viewing: summertime, when Ursa Major is in the northwest.

Arthur's Chariot

(another alias of Ursa Major)

Here you get full value for money because Arthur's Chariot is a stunningly complex, yet easy to see, three dimensional picture comprising thirty stars or so. I found it upside down, me as well as the Chariot!

The Chariot works best when Ursa Major is high in the sky, so find a bean-bag or reclining chair to sit in. With all the high pictures neck-ache can be a problem, and the last thing a star-watcher needs is a pain in the neck.

Before attempting this tricky picture it might be a good idea to familiarise yourself with the Chariot's curves. These are most evident when Ursa Major is low in the north, although the Chariot will be upside down. Should you, whilst checking the curves, happen to see a huge pair of shears snipping along the horizon, don't be surprised.

The Wagon, Charles's Wain, is based on the same stars as the Chariot but is less aerodynamic. The Plough remains elusive. It will, without a doubt, be an impressive 3D image but so far my efforts to unearth it have failed.

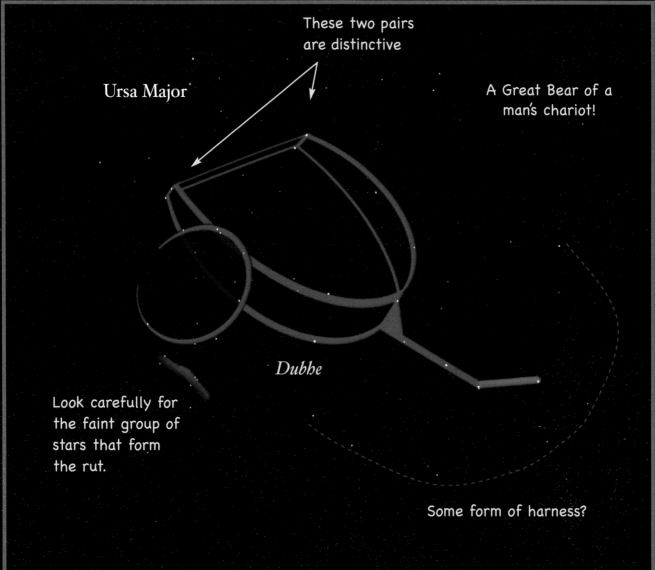

These two pairs
are distinctive

Ursa Major

A Great Bear of a
man's chariot!

Dubhe

Look carefully for
the faint group of
stars that form
the rut.

Some form of harness?

Best viewing: spring and early summer, when Ursa Major is high in the sky.
As Ursa Major sinks towards the northern horizon the Chariot upends – an
action more suited to the Wagon, perhaps.

Every chariot needs a
Charioteer

(constellations Taurus & Auriga: the Charioteer)

Human figures are great fun to find. Basically what you do is this: find a bright star, any bright star, and assume that to be the head. Then look for two fainter stars, the shoulders, they should be close by - if not try another star. From there you need defining points (hands, elbows, bum, knees, feet) of whatever that character is doing, and it could be absolutely anything!

For a start try Vega, Deneb or Altair, the three stars of the Summer Triangle. If it is winter try Rigel in Orion, or Sirius. Arcturus is interesting; there are a couple of characters at least, one I call the Beam Carrier, the other... well, you look.

The Charioteer is toy-soldier simple: a frozen pose, braced and flexing against the chariot's motion; arms outstretched holding the reins. I can only suppose that he does not feature in other star books because, while his upper half is in Auriga, his lower half is in Taurus - not on the same page.

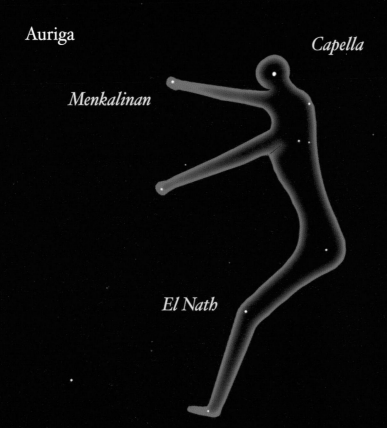

Auriga

Capella

Menkalinan

El Nath

Taurus

Aldebaran

Best viewing: autumn, with Auriga in the northeast, but visible through to April, when he sits on the northern horizon.

When low in the east the Charioteer appears to crawl along the horizon; for that image use Aldebaran as his foot.

Every charioteer is a
Rein Holder

(constellations Auriga, Taurus & Gemini)

When hunting real pictures where does one start when confronted with a name like Menkalinan? A translation* is essential, of course, and Menkalinan translates as Shoulder of the Rein Holder. Such a specific title demands a specific image.

Once you know what you are looking for the next phase is to search for patterns. Look for lines and curves of stars of similar strength; look for repetitive features, i.e. the twin pairs of stars at the rear of the Chariot; look for mirror images, i.e. Pollux, Castor/Menkalinan, Capella; look for distinctive features, i.e. Corona Borealis, Pleiades, Coma Berenices.

In this case the similarity between Auriga and Gemini was important. Auriga had always looked like a fist to me and one night I spotted a similar shape, more suggested than exact, in Gemini. One thing led to another until the reins, a graceful curve of stars from Castor to Procyon, eventually materialised, completing this huge picture. Menkalinan, thankfully, formed part of the shoulder.

*See Index for links to star name translations.

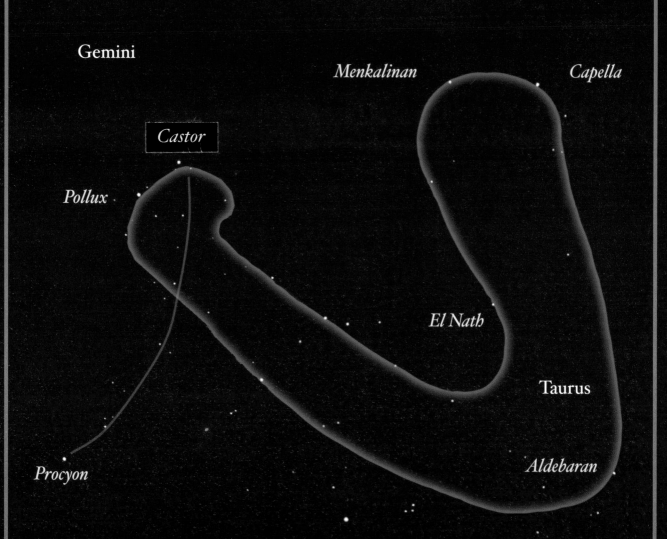

Best viewing: winter, once Procyon has risen in the east; through to spring.

Every rein holder needs a
Black Horse
(constellation Ursa Major)

Alioth means Black Horse, so it should come as no surprise to find a horse in the area. The beauty of the beast is stunning, with its curving profile and distinct leg (a far-side leg is apparent in the night sky).

There is a slight conundrum here as this horse could also be described as a pale rider, being made of faint stars. Some things have yet to be deciphered with absolute certainty and a black horse could, as black horses are glossy, be made from bright stars. If this is the case you should be able to find a similar horse using some of the brighter stars of Ursa Major (imagine two steeds, a span, side by side).

Once you've found the span of horses, take a few moments to work out the span of an archway (refer to the Chariot). Then start pondering the curious linguistic connection... there's more, but that's Little Pig's department.

Ursa Major

Alioth

Dubhe

Could the stars that form the rut of the
chariot's wheel be seen as a suggestion of a
wing? And if so, is there a similar suggestion for
the other wing?
 For this you will need a very clear night.

Best viewing: winter, for a bucking bronco in the northeast; summer for a
rearing stallion in the northwest. A more mellow beast is visible when Ursa
Major is high in the sky.

Unless he happens to be Thor; Thor, the God of War. In which case he needs

A Goat or two

(constellation Auriga)

The Norse god, Thor, needed a pair of goats to pull his chariot. Fortunately for him there happened to be a couple close at hand. Fortunately for us they are still there. Unfortunately for you I'm only going to show you one. Not because I'm hard-hearted but because I know how really satisfying it is to find these pictures for yourself.

Capella: the She-goat, is one of the brightest stars in the sky. To avoid possible confusion with any planet lurking in the area, seek out the little triangle beside Capella. The star at the top of the triangle is called Maaz: the He-goat, and this beast is big. For a clue to his identity check out El Nath: the Butting. Some books assume the Butting refers to the Bull of Taurus, but believe me, bulls do not butt, they gore - which is why I keep goats!

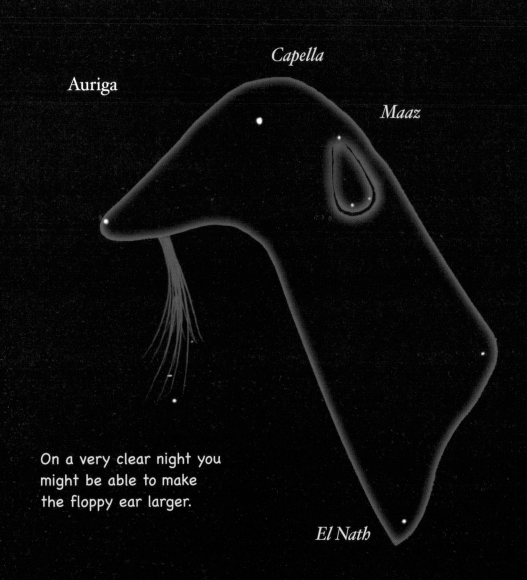

Auriga

Capella

Maaz

On a very clear night you might be able to make the floppy ear larger.

El Nath

Best viewing: autumn into winter, with Auriga just risen in the east. For the butting goat, Aldebaran needs to be visible.

What god of war would be complete without
The Arrow

(constellations Aquila & Sagitta: the Arrow)

Plenty of arrows flying about up there, although the faint, pointed Sagitta is the least arrow-like of them all. However, its Roman name guides our eyes towards the magnificent Arrow in nearby Aquila. (If you have time one night, combine the Sagitta arrow with the Aquila arrow and see what strikes you.)

Both arrows feature in the Odyssey where the hero, Odysseus, starts shooting his wife's suitors. Odysseus, in an act so unlikely of a hard-pressed archer, tips his arrows out by his feet. A curious detail to include, you might think, but it is often through such curious details that star stories reveal themselves.

Those feet of our hero are a fantastic image but, having no star or constellation names to guide us, they belong in Little Pig Star Book territory, sorry.

Should you wish to practise your archery then reach back to Auriga, it's a magic constellation as even the sharpest arrows rebound.

Vega

Sagitta

The fletch is a suggestion
rather than a firm shape.

Altair

Hercules

Aquila

Altair: the Flying, is the brightest star in Aquila: the Eagle.
Note the two stars either side of Altair. Time to test
your mental agility with human figures? Not here, though, in
the night sky where everything is much larger.

Best viewing: late autumn, in the southwest, but visible from May.
Altair is the lowest of the Summer Triangle stars.

What Hunter should be without his
Big Dog

(constellations Orion & Canis Major: the Big Dog)

Herewith another stunningly simple picture. Three bright stars set the scene, with the brightest star of all, Sirius (aka the Dog Star) as the wet, and therefore shiny, nose.

The hunting dog's long snouted head rests on its foreleg, thus depicting the legend where the Big Dog waits patiently, for crumbs, under the table of the feasting Twins. I wonder if the reins dropping from Castor could also be seen as a little morsel thrown for the Dog?

A dog in the manger protects straw from a bull... you could wonder about this curious fable all your life, or you could go star-watching.

With many star animals it is only the head we see. To create a whole beast is complex and, from an I.D. point of view, unnecessary. The ferocious Great Bear and graceful Dolphin are two exceptions.

As the stars rise higher the Dog starts to bark. Not only does it bark, it also catches a Hare.

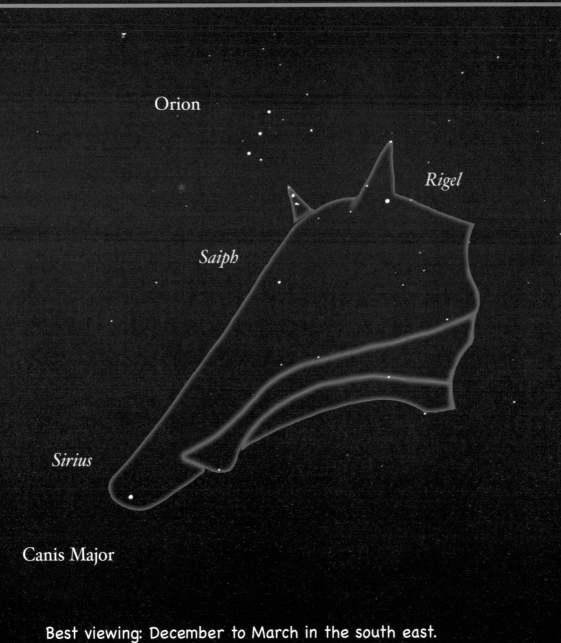

Orion

Rigel

Saiph

Sirius

Canis Major

Best viewing: December to March in the south east.
Watching Sirius rise at dusk is a real treat, so - treat yourself!

Orion, a hunter, loved hunting
The Hare

(constellations Canis Major, Eridanus & Lepus: the Hare)

The Hare is well documented in this area, for both constellation Lepus and star Arneb translate as the Hare.

This Hare is lying low, ears back, motionless. It therefore requires a little more concentration than normal, especially as we have to deal with the bright and distracting Sirius. Cover it with your hand or see it as the head of the Hunter, closing in rapidly.

Once you're familiar with the Hare's head and ear, remove the head and re-view the ear. What do you see?

If you are lucky enough to have a 360° panorama take a look round and round the garden of Planet Earth. You will find two other hares; one smaller and fainter to the north and one much larger and brighter to the east. Until you become a proven hare courser these may take some catching, but give it a go - who knows where they may lead?

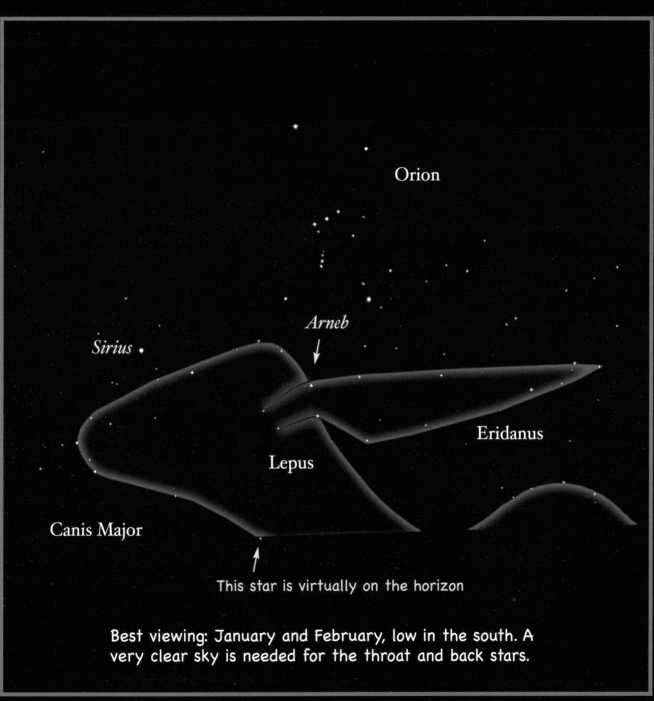

Orion

Arneb

Sirius

Eridanus

Lepus

Canis Major

↑
This star is virtually on the horizon

Best viewing: January and February, low in the south. A very clear sky is needed for the throat and back stars.

Announcing
The Hunter
(constellation Canis Major)

Mirzam is the clue to this figure, for it translates as the Herald or Announcer. This name is thought to refer to the fact that Mirzam rises before Sirius, thus announcing the arrival of the brightest star. As with Aldebaran: the Follower, I could not accept this explanation. Names make sense only if they are image based, the idea that they reflect the motion of the stars falls flat when you consider how many star names there are.

An Announcer is just one possibility for this figure. When seen in conjunction with the Hare this pose suggests a Hunter about to throw or strike. What has he thrown? Did you re-view the Hare's ear? Perhaps he is about to beat the barking Big Dog*.

The figure could also be carrying staves and whirling a sling around its head; a David, you might say, compared to the Goliath of Arthur. Should this little warrior fall then his reward is truly heavenly...

* 'Hush-a- bye a baa-lamb, hush-a-bye a milk cow,
We'll find a little stick to beat the barking bow-wow.'

The Announcer is hitting
something to make a noise,
or perhaps he is carrying a
megaphone.

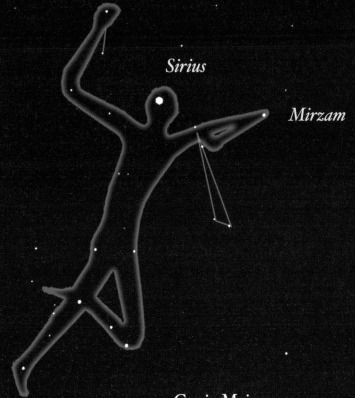

Sirius

Mirzam

The figure appears to be
running towards the Earth
from outer-space.

Canis Major

Best viewing: January to March, in the south. If you time it right the figure
will seem to run on the horizon. For this you will need clean, clear skies.

As pure as driven snow
The Virgins
(constellations Canis Major and Puppis)

Once I turned my attention to Adhara: the Virgins, they took about ten minutes to work out. I couldn't help chuckling. With virgins it's all about the knees - enough said, I hope; if not lie down and experiment. Many times I have found myself adopting a pose or manipulating fingers in order to gain an insight as to how an image might look. Just make sure no-one is watching!

The key to finding these star pictures is to know they exist. Once their existence is accepted it becomes purely a question of time before they reveal both themselves and the humour of our ancestors.

In English myth virgins are associated with the wryneck, a bird of the woodpecker family which has the ability to twist its neck in a most peculiar manner. The most famous of virgins has a hare as her symbol. Should you wonder at these curious connections then enjoy an hour or so searching the stars of a late winter's night. You may even come across another leggy maiden.

Eiger   Monk   Jungfrau, the Virgin

On earth as in heaven. The same rules apply - Jungfrau's knees are tight together and turned away from the eager Eiger. If it wasn't for the Monk...

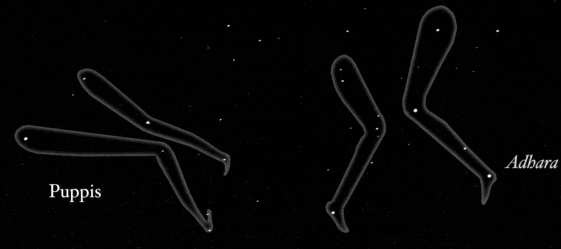

Puppis

Adhara

Canis Major

Best viewing: January to March, low in the south.
These stars form a distinct group. A clear sky is needed.

Fleeced by
The Sheep
(constellation Aries: the Ram)

Reach for the specs again - it's a little 'un. I spent many a chilly, fruitless hour searching for a ram in Aries. With its astrological, as well as constellational significance I reasoned the ram should be an imposing beastie. No luck, not in Aries, at least.

Then, glancing through a list of star names, I noticed Hamal: the Sheep. By this time I was more trusting of star names for image location than I was of constellation names. Since there are precious few stars around Hamal, the Sheep came quickly.

The eyes and blunted nose fell into place easily enough, but 'the watcher became then an eye, a rigidity, an intense out-thrusting and ransacking of thin-spun distance. At last he spoke: "There is wool," he said.'

I lifted that beautiful description from Irish mythology, as it sums up the necessary ocular requirements to fully appreciate the Sheep; in the story the watcher saw dust, not wool.

Aries

The wool that completes
this simple picture can be
seen, on the clearest of
nights, behind the head.
Here one star is just
visible.

Hamal

There are other sheep in the
sky. You might find the same
features in Cygnus (easiest
when in the east).

Best viewing: Late August in the northeast; through to spring. A nice
configuration, emphasised in the southwest, is the Hyades, Pleiades and
Aries ensemble.

Acrobats of the Sea

The Dolphin

(constellations Pegasus and Delphinus: the Dolphin)

Take a late summer's night, add
a starlit sky, look to the east,
clear the head and relax.

1

Pegasus

Look carefully for
the flipper.

There lies the big square of Pegasus; due south lies the faint but
distinctive Delphinus. Breathe in... breathe out... breathe in... breathe
out... Now you're star watching.

2

Stars 1 & 2 form the right
side of the Pegasus square.

Suddenly a shape erupts from the sea, droplets of
water sparkling like stars, a Dolphin! Gracefully arcing
through the night it disappears with hardly a ripple.

Look for the faint
eye and forehead.

Delphinus

This star is called the Tail
of the Dolphin, so is there
yet another dolphin here?

You wait with bated breath. Nothing... nothing. Where is... The shape
rockets high into the sky, twisting, as only the most sublime of
mammals can, so as to fall on its back. It Laughs. You laugh. The others
are watching TV.

I hope these few pages have convinced you that there are real pictures to be found in the stars. Simply knowing they exist will give you confidence in your own sightings.

What you see depends, I suspect, on what Life has thrown your way. If you are familiar with animals then you will see star animals easily. If you are an 'observer of people' then human figures should pose no problems, even unearthly ones...

The tale of Aladdin was fresh in Jacqi's mind when she dropped over one evening. We were chatting outside, looking at the stars, and I showed her the Fish, flapping on the northern horizon. She immediately said it looked like Aladdin's lamp - result!

The most satisfying moments, to me, are when other people find star pictures. It does seem that some people are naturally gifted in this respect:

Jesse had only been star-watching for five minutes, during which time I tried to explain how the best pictures work; follow stars of even strength, use bright stars at defining points. 'I can see a panther,' he said, 'with a gold collar and chain.' Can you?

Like many images the panther works better in the stars than it does on paper. The vast expanse of the night sky provides the space (and the peace) required for our minds to perfect the pictures.

Here's the collar.

Panther in Ursa Major

Happy stargazing!

Shears over the Cowhouse

All star photography by Nick

This is Little Pig, a keen star-watcher. In his series of star books (see over) he shows you how to make Real Pictures come alive. It is actually quite amazing.

~

If you find yourself addicted to the task of rediscovering the real pictures and would like to become actively involved in the quest, then check out

www.realstarpictures.com

where you can log your sightings. The best will feature in future books.

Six Little Pig Star Books that bring the Real Pictures alive:

Jack and Jill
The Lion and the Unicorn
Goosey Goosey Gander
The Loch Ness Monster Myth
Three Blind Mice
'Book X'

A note about Nursery Rhymes

Nursery rhymes are not nonsense, nor are they simply
for children. They are tools for learning star pictures
and, as such, have carried a message, encoded in the
safest possible form, down through the generations.
Now is the time, it seems, for the message to be seen.

www.littlepigpublications.com

Index

Page titles in **bold**; star names in *italics*.

For *star name* translations try: www.icoproject.org/star.html or www.naic.edu/~gibson/starnames